Alan Haughton

C000004782

Rhythm&Rag
for Clarinet

Contents

1. March Past *2*
2. Walk On *3*
3. Prelude *4*
4. Wagons Roll *6*
5. Blues 9 *8*
6. Keep Cool *9*
7. Bird of Paradise *10*
8. Short Stop *12*
9. Straight Fours *14*
10. Nocturne *16*
11. Warm Up *18*
12. Opus Rag *20*
13. Cakewalk *22*
14. Little Girl *24*
15. Jazz Three *26*
16. Jazz It Up *28*
17. Monkey Nuts *30*

**The Associated Board of
the Royal Schools of Music**

for M and D

Rhythm & Rag for Clarinet

ALAN HAUGHTON

1. March Past

© 1998 by The Associated Board of the Royal Schools of Music

AB 2697

2. Walk On

3. Prelude

4. Wagons Roll

5. Blues 9

6. Keep Cool

7. Bird of Paradise

8. Short Stop

9. Straight Fours

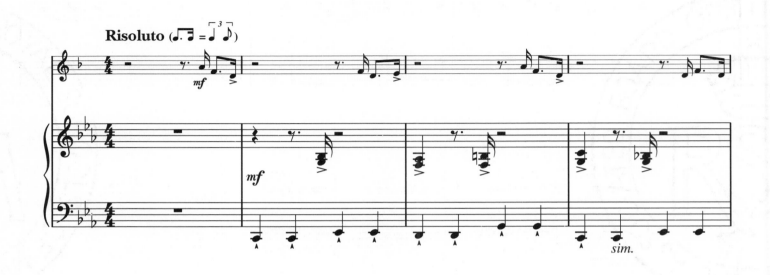

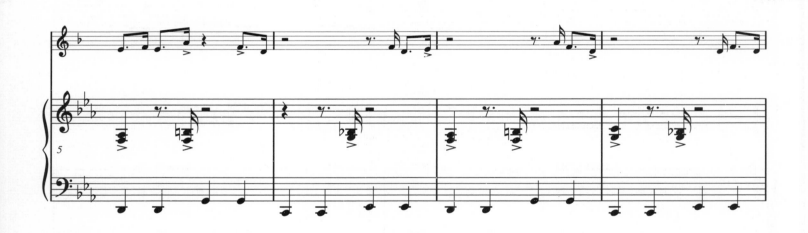

10. Nocturne

11. Warm Up

12. Opus Rag

13. Cakewalk

14. Little Girl

15. Jazz Three

16. Jazz It Up

17. Monkey Nuts

Printed in England by
Caligraving Limited, Thetford, Norfolk

Alan Haughton

Rhythm&Rag
for Clarinet

Contents

1. March Past *2*
2. Walk On *2*
3. Prelude *2*
4. Wagons Roll *3*
5. Blues 9 *4*
6. Keep Cool *4*
7. Bird of Paradise *5*
8. Short Stop *5*
9. Straight Fours *6*
10. Nocturne *6*
11. Warm Up *7*
12. Opus Rag *8*
13. Cakewalk *8*
14. Little Girl *9*
15. Jazz Three *10*
16. Jazz It Up *11*
17. Monkey Nuts *12*

The Associated Board of
the Royal Schools of Music

for M and D

Rhythm & Rag for Clarinet

CLARINET in B♭

ALAN HAUGHTON

1. March Past

2. Walk On

3. Prelude

© 1998 by The Associated Board of the Royal Schools of Music

AB 2697

4. Wagons Roll

5. Blues 9

6. Keep Cool

7. Bird of Paradise

8. Short Stop

9. Straight Fours

10. Nocturne

11. Warm Up

12. Opus Rag

13. Cakewalk

14. Little Girl

15. Jazz Three